PILOT TO CO-PILOT

A story to share and take the scare out of Parkinson's Disease.

Gloria Gottesman

Illustrations by Ellie Gottesman

ISBN-13: 978-0-9911557-2-9
JayEddy Publishing
Mercer Island, Washington

This book is dedicated to everyone living with Parkinson's.
Wage the war!

My name is Lucas and in 21 days I will be 11-years-old.
I live with my mom, dad, and my 14-year-old know-it-all
sister, Sophie. My rescue dog, Trouble, is no trouble at all.

I wear glasses and smile a lot, except when Sophie slams her door.

I'm shorter than most of my friends, but I can run fast and I'm a super soccer player.

Miss Fujii, my fifth grade teacher, gave our class an assignment to write about a hero. "A hero is someone who is admired for his or her actions in difficult situations," she said.

Just about everyone in class raised their hand.

"How about Superman? Is that okay?" Harry asked.

Amanda announced, "My Aunt Lucy, an army nurse, is my hero."

"I'm going to write about Mr. Robinson, the firefighter

who lives on our block," Nolan said,

I knew who my hero would be as soon as Miss Fuijii gave us the project.

Pilot to Co-Pilot

By Lucas   5th Grade   Miss Fujii

Poppi Paul, my grandpa, is my hero. He has a disease called Parkinson's that he battles every day. At first, I was afraid I could get Parkinson's like a cold or the flu. I was happy to learn you can't catch Parkinson's from another person. I hug and play with Poppi Paul all I want. No problem!

When I was six, I thought that Poppi got Parkinson's from "parking-in-the-sun." I would say, "Poppi, please park in the shade." Now I know Parkinson's has nothing to do with the sun. Parkinson's was named after a Dr. Parkinson who wrote about it almost two-hundred-years ago.

Our brain controls all our movements. Brain cells talk to each other using nerves that are like electrical wires. Instead of electricity, the nerves release special chemicals to pass on instructions. One of these chemicals is called dopamine.

People with Parkinson's don't make enough dopamine for the brain to send instructions to the body.

Poppi takes medicine to help his brain replace the missing dopamine.

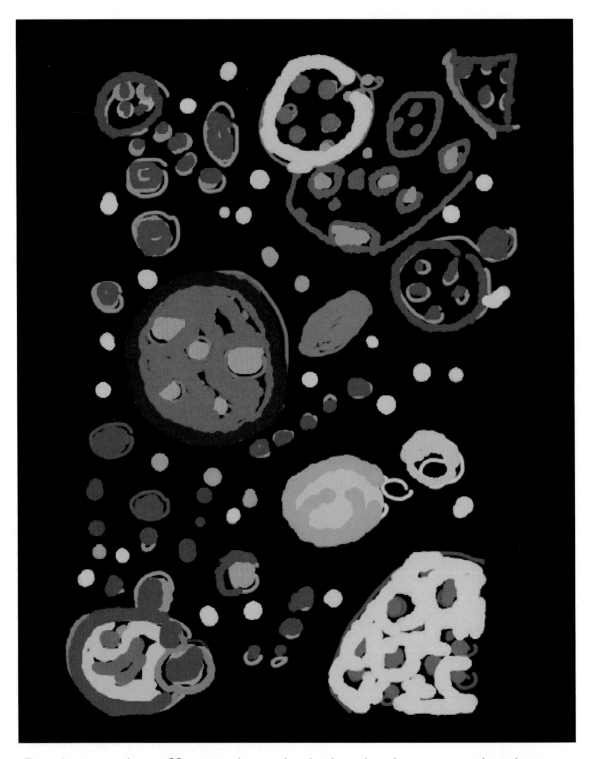

Parkinson's affects the whole body but mostly the way Poppi Paul moves.

Now, let me tell you about Poppi Paul. He seems to know what I'm thinking. I don't have to say anything, he just knows. We laugh at the same jokes. He is my biggest fan, always rooting for me at my soccer and baseball games.

Two years ago, Poppi hung a
tennis ball on a rope and attached it to a tree so I
could practice hitting baseballs.
We used to play lots of catch, but now that
seems too hard for Poppi. Sometimes, he trips
and falls. With Parkinson's, his brain doesn't
always tell him to lift his feet high enough.

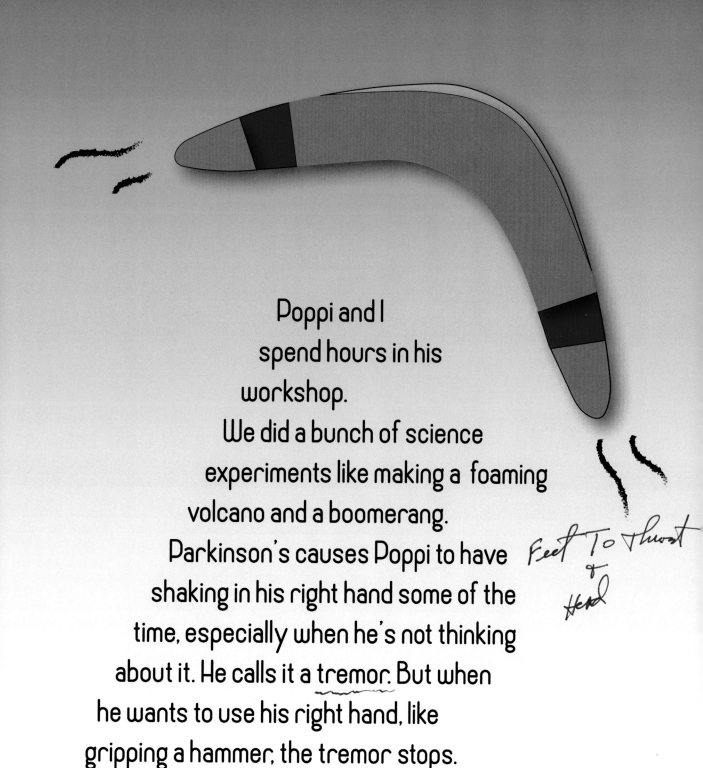

Poppi and I
spend hours in his
workshop.
We did a bunch of science
experiments like making a foaming
volcano and a boomerang.
Parkinson's causes Poppi to have
shaking in his right hand some of the
time, especially when he's not thinking
about it. He calls it a tremor. But when
he wants to use his right hand, like
gripping a hammer, the tremor stops.

Feet To Throat
&
Head

brrrr

Sometimes, Poppi's feet get stuck on the ground. He told me this is called "freezing," but it has nothing to do with being cold.

"You can't judge a book by its cover..."

Everyone with Parkinson's is affected differently.
Some have <u>tremors</u>, some fall, and some have
difficulty <u>speaking</u>. Some of Poppi's friends with
Parkinson's can't smile anymore because the
<u>muscles of the face</u> don't move. It's like they are
wearing a mask. Poppi says they are smiling on
the inside.

Eye (above "face")

Right Eye

Poppi, Trouble and I take lots of walks. Exercise
is very important for people with Parkinson's.
We play a game called Pilot to Co-pilot. Poppi
Paul is the pilot and I am second in command.
We pretend to fly all around the world.

"Poppi, are you ready for take-off?"
"Ready, Co-pilot Lucas. I think we'll head to New York City.
"Yes Sir, Captain. We are expecting rough weather so keep
the nose up."
'The nose up' is our secret code that means, 'Poppi keep
your head up and walk with good posture.'

People with Parkinson's often hunch over and Poppi wants
to train his muscles so he stands up straight.
I say, "Captain, let the jets do the work."
In our code, "let the jets do the work" means swing your
arms back and forth and take big, giant steps.

YES
ANNA

18

Parkinson's causes Poppi to talk so quietly that I can't always hear him. ✓
So I run ahead and pretend like I'm at the other end of a big plane and we practice speaking loudly.
I yell, "Co-pilot to Pilot. Great day for flying. Don't you think?"
"I do," Poppi says.
"Repeat louder."
"I do. I do, Co-pilot Lucas. Maybe we should touch down and have an ice-cream cone."

YES!

Poppi loves taking boxing classes. He rides a bike in his den.
"Find the exercises you like and then you won't have any problem
doing them," he says.

ZZZZZzzzzzzzzzzzzzzzzzzzzzzz

Poppi gets tired a lot. Poppi thinks it's because of the Parkinson's, or his medicine, or his age or all three. When he naps, I spend the time with Grandma who is Poppi's main caregiver. *Thank You Nowna*

Grandma tells me, "Parkinson's keeps changing, so we will have new challenges to face. The good news is that Parkinson's research is going on all over the world and new drugs are available for Poppi all the time. Also, a special brain surgery helps many people with Parkinson's."

ZZZZZzzzzzzzzzzzzzzzzzzzzzzz

Poppi always tells me how much he appreciates our whole family. I think it's true. I see how he lights up when I walk in the room. I know he loves me. I just hope he knows how much I love him back.

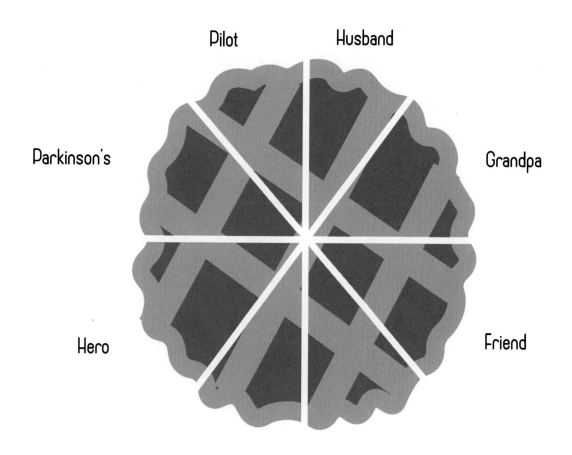

Pilot

Husband

Parkinson's

Grandpa

Hero

Friend

Poppi likes to think of himself as an ordinary guy with an
EXTRA-ORDINARY condition.
Parkinson's is just one part of him.
Right now, he is showing me what it takes to be a hero. A hero
does not necessarily look like Superman or a soldier. A hero
is someone who meets each day with courage.

"Thank you, Lucas, for sharing your story," Miss Fujii said. "Boys and girls, we have a surprise for you. Lucas' Poppi is here to teach us how to build that foaming volcano that Lucas wrote about in his story."

Poppi Paul comes from around the corner
where he was hiding and listening to me read.
Everyone claps really hard. I'm so proud.
Poppi walks with big strides to the front of the room.
He must have gotten something caught in his eye
because he has tears rolling down his cheek.
"A volcano," he begins.

The end

Acknowledgements

My first shoutout goes to my talented and loving granddaughter, Ellie Gottesman, who spent countless hours illustrating and bringing this book "home." How lucky am I? You have been so supportive and I love you more than I can express.

Thanks to Peter Kolb, a Person with Parkinson's who corresponded with me from across the world in South Africa and contributed two drawings: Pilot to Co-pilot and Balance.

I modeled the grandpa, Poppi, after my husband, Jim, who I believe to be the best grandpa a child could have. He is also my computer guru.

I modeled Poppi's symptoms after some of my own and those of several friends with Parkinson's.

The Northwest Parkinson's Foundation (NWPF.ORG) has been a rock, helping me and other Parkies meet their every day challenges. All proceeds of Pilot to Co-pilot go to the Northwest Parkinson's Foundation
Send donations to

NWPF
7525 SE 24th Street   Ste 300
Mercer Island, WA 98040, USA

37217070R00018

Made in the USA
San Bernardino, CA
28 May 2019